Girl, Stop Apologizing

A Shame-free Plan for Embracing and Achieving Your Goals

A Journal

ISBN-13: 978-1-951161-74-3

Girl, Stop Apologizing

This Journal Belongs To

_____

_____

How to Use This Journal To Achieve Your Goals

Complete beginners can begin using this Journal for Girl, Stop Apologizing A Shame-Free Plan for Embracing and Achieving Your Goals by Rachel Hollis to get immediate help of the major lessons and Quotes found in this book.

The goal of this Journal is to help even the newest readers to begin applying major lessons from Girl, Stop Apologizing A Shame-Free Plan for Embracing and Achieving Your Goals by Rachel Hollis. Results have shown us that Journaling the Things you're thankful for each day will help you achieve your goals.

By using this Journal, readers will find Awesome and Life-changing quotes by Rachel that we believed were major in defining the crucial messages of the author in the book.

There are Spaces to jot down, 3 things you are thankful for and 7 Goals for Next week, also Space to track your habits and hydration level. Take out a pencil, pen, or whatever digital technology you would put to use to jot down, implement, and make happen.

And don't forget to have fun - While at it. This Journal Will aid in your path to growth, confidence, and believing in yourself.

"
A goal
is a dream with
it's work boots on.
- Rachel Hollis

3 Things I am Thankful For »

7 Goals For Next Week »»»»»

Notes »

Getting Things Done For The Week of: _____

things to do

Habit Tracker

HABIT	S	M	T	W	T	F	S	REWARD

Water
(Check The Circle For 8 Glass Daily)

Girl you Got This!

SUN	MON	TUES	WED	THUR	FRI	SAT
○○○○	○○○○	○○○○	○○○○	○○○○	○○○○	○○○○
○○○○	○○○○	○○○○	○○○○	○○○○	○○○○	○○○○

3 Things I am Thankful For »

7 Goals For Next Week »»»»

Notes »

Getting Things Done For The Week of: _____

things to do

~ Habit Tracker ~

HABIT	S	M	T	W	T	F	S	REWARD

Water
(Check The Circle For 8 Glass Daily)

SUN	MON	TUES	WED	THUR	FRI	SAT
○○○○	○○○○	○○○○	○○○○	○○○○	○○○○	○○○○
○○○○	○○○○	○○○○	○○○○	○○○○	○○○○	○○○○

Girl you got This!

3 Things I am Thankful For »

7 Goals For Next Week »»»»

Notes »

Getting Things Done For The Week of: _____

things to do

Habit Tracker

HABIT	S	M	T	W	T	F	S	REWARD

Water
(Check The Circle For 8 Glass Daily)

SUN	MON	TUES	WED	THUR	FRI	SAT
○○○○ ○○○○	○○○○ ○○○○	○○○○ ○○○○	○○○○ ○○○○	○○○○ ○○○○	○○○○ ○○○○	○○○○ ○○○○

Girl you Got This!

3 Things I am Thankful For »

7 Goals For Next Week »»»»

Notes »

Getting Things Done For The Week of: _____

things to do

Habit Tracker

HABIT	S	M	T	W	T	F	S	REWARD

Water
(Check The Circle For 8 Glass Daily)

SUN	MON	TUES	WED	THUR	FRI	SAT
○○○○○	○○○○○	○○○○○	○○○○○	○○○○○	○○○○○	○○○○○
○○○○○	○○○○○	○○○○○	○○○○○	○○○○○	○○○○○	○○○○○

Girl you got this!

Dreams I made Happen This Month

"

Lazy will always
try and drag
you back down
to lazy.
- Rachel Hollis

3 Things I am Thankful For »

7 Goals For Next Week »»»»

Notes »

Getting Things Done For The Week of: _____

things to do

Habit Tracker

HABIT	S	M	T	W	T	F	S	REWARD

Water
(Check The Circle For 8 Glass Daily)

Girl you Got This!

SUN	MON	TUES	WED	THUR	FRI	SAT
◊◊◊◊ ◊◊◊◊	◊◊◊◊ ◊◊◊◊	◊◊◊◊ ◊◊◊◊	◊◊◊◊ ◊◊◊◊	◊◊◊◊ ◊◊◊◊	◊◊◊◊ ◊◊◊◊	◊◊◊◊ ◊◊◊◊

3 Things I am Thankful For »

7 Goals For Next Week »»»»

Notes »

Getting Things Done For The Week of: _____

things to do

Habit Tracker

HABIT	S	M	T	W	T	F	S	REWARD

Water
(Check The Circle For 8 Glass Daily)

SUN	MON	TUES	WED	THUR	FRI	SAT

Girl you Got This!

3 Things I am Thankful For »

7 Goals For Next Week »»»»

Notes »

Getting Things Done For The Week of: _____

things to do

Habit Tracker

HABIT	S	M	T	W	T	F	S	REWARD

Water
(Check The Circle For 8 Glass Daily)

Girl you Got This!

SUN	MON	TUES	WED	THUR	FRI	SAT
⬤⬤⬤⬤	⬤⬤⬤⬤	⬤⬤⬤⬤	⬤⬤⬤⬤	⬤⬤⬤⬤	⬤⬤⬤⬤	⬤⬤⬤⬤
⬤⬤⬤⬤	⬤⬤⬤⬤	⬤⬤⬤⬤	⬤⬤⬤⬤	⬤⬤⬤⬤	⬤⬤⬤⬤	⬤⬤⬤⬤

3 Things I am Thankful For »

7 Goals For Next Week »»»»

Notes »

Getting Things Done For The Week of: _____

things to do

Habit Tracker

HABIT	S	M	T	W	T	F	S	REWARD

Water
(Check The Circle For 8 Glass Daily)

Girl you Got This!

SUN	MON	TUES	WED	THUR	FRI	SAT
○○○○	○○○○	○○○○	○○○○	○○○○	○○○○	○○○○
○○○○	○○○○	○○○○	○○○○	○○○○	○○○○	○○○○

Dreams I made Happen This Month

"

I can achieve
anything
if I'm willing to work
for it. Not because
I'm especially gifted,
but because
I'm dedicated to
improving along
the way.
- Rachel Hollis

3 Things I am Thankful For »

7 Goals For Next Week »»»»

Notes »

Getting Things Done For The Week of: _____

things to do

Habit Tracker

HABIT	S	M	T	W	T	F	S	REWARD

Water
(Check The Circle For 8 Glass Daily)

girl you got this!

SUN	MON	TUES	WED	THUR	FRI	SAT
○○○○	○○○○	○○○○	○○○○	○○○○	○○○○	○○○○
○○○○	○○○○	○○○○	○○○○	○○○○	○○○○	○○○○

3 Things I am Thankful For »

7 Goals For Next Week »»»»

Notes »

Getting Things Done For The Week of: _____

things to do

Habit Tracker

HABIT	S	M	T	W	T	F	S	REWARD

Water
(Check The Circle For 8 Glass Daily)

SUN	MON	TUES	WED	THUR	FRI	SAT
○○○○	○○○○	○○○○	○○○○	○○○○	○○○○	○○○○
○○○○	○○○○	○○○○	○○○○	○○○○	○○○○	○○○○

girl you got this!

3 Things I am Thankful For »

7 Goals For Next Week »»»»

Notes »

Getting Things Done For The Week of: _____

things to do

Habit Tracker

HABIT	S	M	T	W	T	F	S	REWARD

Water
(Check The Circle For 8 Glass Daily)

SUN	MON	TUES	WED	THUR	FRI	SAT
○○○○	○○○○	○○○○	○○○○	○○○○	○○○○	○○○○
○○○○	○○○○	○○○○	○○○○	○○○○	○○○○	○○○○

you you got this!

3 Things I am Thankful For »

7 Goals For Next Week »»»»

Notes »

Getting Things Done For The Week Of: _____

things to do

Habit Tracker

HABIT	S	M	T	W	T	F	S	REWARD

Water
(Check The Circle For 8 Glass Daily)

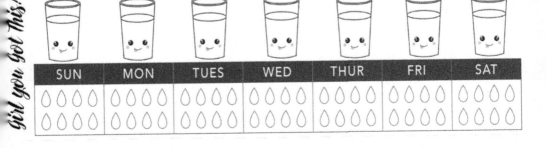

SUN	MON	TUES	WED	THUR	FRI	SAT
○○○○	○○○○	○○○○	○○○○	○○○○	○○○○	○○○○
○○○○	○○○○	○○○○	○○○○	○○○○	○○○○	○○○○

Girl you got this!

Dreams I made Happen This Month

"

There's a big
difference between
gratitude for your life
and blind acceptance
of whatever comes
your way.
- Rachel Hollis

3 Things I am Thankful For »

7 Goals For Next Week »»»»

Notes »

Getting Things Done For The Week of: _____

things to do

Habit Tracker

HABIT	S	M	T	W	T	F	S	REWARD

Water
(Check The Circle For 8 Glass Daily)

SUN	MON	TUES	WED	THUR	FRI	SAT

Girl you Got This!

3 Things I am Thankful For »

7 Goals For Next Week »»»»

Notes »

Getting Things Done For The Week of: _____

things to do

Habit Tracker

HABIT	S	M	T	W	T	F	S	REWARD

Water
(Check The Circle For 8 Glass Daily)

SUN	MON	TUES	WED	THUR	FRI	SAT

Girl you Got This!

3 Things I am Thankful For »

7 Goals For Next Week »»»»

Notes »

Getting Things Done For The Week of: _____

things to do

Habit Tracker

HABIT	S	M	T	W	T	F	S	REWARD

Water
(Check The Circle For 8 Glass Daily)

Girl you got This!

SUN	MON	TUES	WED	THUR	FRI	SAT
○○○○	○○○○	○○○○	○○○○	○○○○	○○○○	○○○○
○○○○	○○○○	○○○○	○○○○	○○○○	○○○○	○○○○

3 Things I am Thankful For »

7 Goals For Next Week »»»»

Notes »

Getting Things Done For The Week of: _____

things to do

Habit Tracker

HABIT	S	M	T	W	T	F	S	REWARD

Water
(Check The Circle For 8 Glass Daily)

girl you got this!

Dreams I made Happen This Month

"

The best advice
I know of in this
situation is, if you
want to change
someone else,
change yourself.
- Rachel Hollis

3 Things I am Thankful For »

7 Goals For Next Week »»»»

Notes »

"

The best advice
I know of in this
situation is, if you
want to change
someone else,
change yourself.
- Rachel Hollis

3 Things I am Thankful For »

7 Goals For Next Week »»»»

Notes »

Getting Things Done For The Week Of: _____

things to do

Habit Tracker

HABIT	S	M	T	W	T	F	S	REWARD

Water
(Check The Circle For 8 Glass Daily)

SUN	MON	TUES	WED	THUR	FRI	SAT
○○○○	○○○○	○○○○	○○○○	○○○○	○○○○	○○○○
○○○○	○○○○	○○○○	○○○○	○○○○	○○○○	○○○○

girl you got this!

3 Things I am Thankful For »

7 Goals For Next Week »»»»

Notes »

Getting Things Done For The Week of: _____

things to do

~ Habit Tracker ~

HABIT	S	M	T	W	T	F	S	REWARD

Water
(Check The Circle For 8 Glass Daily)

SUN	MON	TUES	WED	THUR	FRI	SAT

you you you this!

3 Things I am Thankful For »

7 Goals For Next Week »»»»

Notes »

Getting Things Done For The Week of: _____

things to do

Habit Tracker

HABIT	S	M	T	W	T	F	S	REWARD

Water
(Check The Circle For 8 Glass Daily)

SUN	MON	TUES	WED	THUR	FRI	SAT
○○○○	○○○○	○○○○	○○○○	○○○○	○○○○	○○○○
○○○○	○○○○	○○○○	○○○○	○○○○	○○○○	○○○○

yay you got this!

3 Things I am Thankful For »

7 Goals For Next Week »»»»

Notes »

Getting Things Done For The Week of: _____

things to do

Habit Tracker

HABIT	S	M	T	W	T	F	S	REWARD

Water
(Check The Circle For 8 Glass Daily)

you got this!

Dreams I made Happen This Month

"
You want to be more confident? Hang out with people who are.
- Rachel Hollis

3 Things I am Thankful For »

7 Goals For Next Week »»»»

Notes »

Getting Things Done For The Week of: _____

things to do

~ Habit Tracker ~

HABIT	S	M	T	W	T	F	S	REWARD

Water
(Check The Circle For 8 Glass Daily)

Girl you Got This!

SUN	MON	TUES	WED	THUR	FRI	SAT
○○○○ ○○○○	○○○○ ○○○○	○○○○ ○○○○	○○○○ ○○○○	○○○○ ○○○○	○○○○ ○○○○	○○○○ ○○○○

3 Things I am Thankful For »

7 Goals For Next Week »»»»

Notes »

Getting Things Done For The Week of: _____

things to do

Habit Tracker

HABIT	S	M	T	W	T	F	S	REWARD

Water
(Check The Circle For 8 Glass Daily)

SUN	MON	TUES	WED	THUR	FRI	SAT
○○○○	○○○○	○○○○	○○○○	○○○○	○○○○	○○○○
○○○○	○○○○	○○○○	○○○○	○○○○	○○○○	○○○○

girl you got this!

3 Things I am Thankful For »

7 Goals For Next Week »»»

Notes »

Getting Things Done For The Week of: _____

things to do

Habit Tracker

HABIT	S	M	T	W	T	F	S	REWARD

Water
(Check The Circle For 8 Glass Daily)

SUN	MON	TUES	WED	THUR	FRI	SAT
○○○○	○○○○	○○○○	○○○○	○○○○	○○○○	○○○○
○○○○	○○○○	○○○○	○○○○	○○○○	○○○○	○○○○

you you got this!

3 Things I am Thankful For »

7 Goals For Next Week »»»»

Notes »

Getting Things Done For The Week of: _____

things to do

Habit Tracker

HABIT	S	M	T	W	T	F	S	REWARD

Water
(Check The Circle For 8 Glass Daily)

SUN	MON	TUES	WED	THUR	FRI	SAT
○○○○	○○○○	○○○○	○○○○	○○○○	○○○○	○○○○
○○○○	○○○○	○○○○	○○○○	○○○○	○○○○	○○○○

get you got me!

Dreams I made Happen This Month

"

It's going to be a journey and you're going to have to fight to get to where you want to go, but it's also going to be worth it.

- Rachel Hollis

3 Things I am Thankful For »

7 Goals For Next Week »»»»

Notes »

Getting Things Done For The Week of: _____

Habit Tracker

HABIT	S	M	T	W	T	F	S	REWARD

Water
(Check The Circle For 8 Glass Daily)

SUN	MON	TUES	WED	THUR	FRI	SAT
○○○○	○○○○	○○○○	○○○○	○○○○	○○○○	○○○○
○○○○	○○○○	○○○○	○○○○	○○○○	○○○○	○○○○

3 Things I am Thankful For »

7 Goals For Next Week »»»»

Notes »

Getting Things Done For The Week of: _____

things to do

Habit Tracker

HABIT	S	M	T	W	T	F	S	REWARD

Water
(Check The Circle For 8 Glass Daily)

you you you this!

SUN	MON	TUES	WED	THUR	FRI	SAT
○○○○	○○○○	○○○○	○○○○	○○○○	○○○○	○○○○
○○○○	○○○○	○○○○	○○○○	○○○○	○○○○	○○○○

3 Things I am Thankful For »

7 Goals For Next Week »»»»

Notes »

Getting Things Done For The Week of: _____

things to do

Habit Tracker

HABIT	S	M	T	W	T	F	S	REWARD

Water
(Check The Circle For 8 Glass Daily)

you you you this!

SUN	MON	TUES	WED	THUR	FRI	SAT
○○○○	○○○○	○○○○	○○○○	○○○○	○○○○	○○○○
○○○○	○○○○	○○○○	○○○○	○○○○	○○○○	○○○○

3 Things I am Thankful For »

7 Goals For Next Week »»»»

Notes »

Getting Things Done For The Week of: _____

things to do

Habit Tracker

HABIT	S	M	T	W	T	F	S	REWARD

Water
(Check The Circle For 8 Glass Daily)

Girl you Got This!

SUN	MON	TUES	WED	THUR	FRI	SAT
○○○○	○○○○	○○○○	○○○○	○○○○	○○○○	○○○○
○○○○	○○○○	○○○○	○○○○	○○○○	○○○○	○○○○

Dreams I made Happen This Month

"
Anything other than
death is temporary.
The problem is that
you're letting
a short-term choice
become your
long-term decision.
- Rachel Hollis

3 Things I am Thankful For »

7 Goals For Next Week »»»»

Notes »

Getting Things Done For The Week of: _____

things to do

Habit Tracker

HABIT	S	M	T	W	T	F	S	REWARD

Water
(Check The Circle For 8 Glass Daily)

SUN	MON	TUES	WED	THUR	FRI	SAT
○○○○	○○○○	○○○○	○○○○	○○○○	○○○○	○○○○
○○○○	○○○○	○○○○	○○○○	○○○○	○○○○	○○○○

girl you got this!

3 Things I am Thankful For »

7 Goals For Next Week »»»»

Notes »

Getting Things Done For The Week of: _____

things to do

Habit Tracker

HABIT	S	M	T	W	T	F	S	REWARD

Water
(Check The Circle For 8 Glass Daily)

SUN	MON	TUES	WED	THUR	FRI	SAT
○○○○	○○○○	○○○○	○○○○	○○○○	○○○○	○○○○
○○○○	○○○○	○○○○	○○○○	○○○○	○○○○	○○○○

3 Things I am Thankful For »

7 Goals For Next Week »»»»

Notes »

Getting Things Done For The Week of: _____

things to do

Habit Tracker

HABIT	S	M	T	W	T	F	S	REWARD

Water
(Check The Circle For 8 Glass Daily)

SUN	MON	TUES	WED	THUR	FRI	SAT
OOOO	OOOO	OOOO	OOOO	OOOO	OOOO	OOOO
OOOO	OOOO	OOOO	OOOO	OOOO	OOOO	OOOO

you you got this!

3 Things I am Thankful For »

7 Goals For Next Week »»»»

Notes »

Getting Things Done For The Week of: _____

things to do

Habit Tracker

HABIT	S	M	T	W	T	F	S	REWARD

Water
(Check The Circle For 8 Glass Daily)

SUN	MON	TUES	WED	THUR	FRI	SAT
○○○○	○○○○	○○○○	○○○○	○○○○	○○○○	○○○○
○○○○	○○○○	○○○○	○○○○	○○○○	○○○○	○○○○

you you you this!

Dreams I made Happen This Month

" Failure means that you're living. Failure means that you're trying. - Rachel Hollis

3 Things I am Thankful For »

7 Goals For Next Week »»»»

Notes »

Getting Things Done For The Week of: _____

things to do

Habit Tracker

HABIT	S	M	T	W	T	F	S	REWARD

Water
(Check The Circle For 8 Glass Daily)

SUN	MON	TUES	WED	THUR	FRI	SAT
○○○○ ○○○○	○○○○ ○○○○	○○○○ ○○○○	○○○○ ○○○○	○○○○ ○○○○	○○○○ ○○○○	○○○○ ○○○○

3 Things I am Thankful For »

7 Goals For Next Week »»»»

Notes »

Getting Things Done For The Week of: _____

things to do

Habit Tracker

HABIT	S	M	T	W	T	F	S	REWARD

Water
(Check The Circle For 8 Glass Daily)

you you you you mys!

SUN	MON	TUES	WED	THUR	FRI	SAT
○○○○	○○○○	○○○○	○○○○	○○○○	○○○○	○○○○
○○○○	○○○○	○○○○	○○○○	○○○○	○○○○	○○○○

3 Things I am Thankful For »

7 Goals For Next Week »»»»

Notes »

Getting Things Done For The Week of: _____

Habit Tracker

HABIT	S	M	T	W	T	F	S	REWARD

Water
(Check The Circle For 8 Glass Daily)

SUN	MON	TUES	WED	THUR	FRI	SAT
○○○○	○○○○	○○○○	○○○○	○○○○	○○○○	○○○○
○○○○	○○○○	○○○○	○○○○	○○○○	○○○○	○○○○

girl you got this!

3 Things I am Thankful For »

7 Goals For Next Week »»»»

Notes »

Getting Things Done For The Week of: _____

things to do

Habit Tracker

HABIT	S	M	T	W	T	F	S	REWARD

Water
(Check The Circle For 8 Glass Daily)

Girl you Got This!

SUN	MON	TUES	WED	THUR	FRI	SAT
○○○○○	○○○○○	○○○○○	○○○○○	○○○○○	○○○○○	○○○○○
○○○○○	○○○○○	○○○○○	○○○○○	○○○○○	○○○○○	○○○○○

Dreams I made Happen This Month

" It happens when you stop asking permission to be yourself.
- Rachel Hollis

3 Things I am Thankful For »

7 Goals For Next Week »»»»

Notes »

Getting Things Done For The Week of: _____

things to do

Habit Tracker

HABIT	S	M	T	W	T	F	S	REWARD

Water
(Check The Circle For 8 Glass Daily)

SUN	MON	TUES	WED	THUR	FRI	SAT
◊◊◊◊	◊◊◊◊	◊◊◊◊	◊◊◊◊	◊◊◊◊	◊◊◊◊	◊◊◊◊
◊◊◊◊	◊◊◊◊	◊◊◊◊	◊◊◊◊	◊◊◊◊	◊◊◊◊	◊◊◊◊

you you got this!

3 Things I am Thankful For »

7 Goals For Next Week »»»»

Notes »

Getting Things Done For The Week of: _____

things to do

Habit Tracker

HABIT	S	M	T	W	T	F	S	REWARD

Water
(Check The Circle For 8 Glass Daily)

SUN	MON	TUES	WED	THUR	FRI	SAT

you you got this!

3 Things I am Thankful For »

7 Goals For Next Week »»»»

Notes »

Getting Things Done For The Week of: _____

things to do

～Habit Tracker～

HABIT	S	M	T	W	T	F	S	REWARD

Water
(Check The Circle For 8 Glass Daily)

SUN	MON	TUES	WED	THUR	FRI	SAT
○○○○	○○○○	○○○○	○○○○	○○○○	○○○○	○○○○
○○○○	○○○○	○○○○	○○○○	○○○○	○○○○	○○○○

you got this!

3 Things I am Thankful For »

7 Goals For Next Week »»»

Notes »

Getting Things Done For The Week of: _____

things to do

Habit Tracker

HABIT	S	M	T	W	T	F	S	REWARD

Water
(Check The Circle For 8 Glass Daily)

SUN	MON	TUES	WED	THUR	FRI	SAT
○○○○	○○○○	○○○○	○○○○	○○○○	○○○○	○○○○
○○○○	○○○○	○○○○	○○○○	○○○○	○○○○	○○○○

Dreams I made Happen This Month

You cannot control
the circumstances
of your life; you can
only control your
reaction to them.
- Rachel Hollis

3 Things I am Thankful For »

7 Goals For Next Week »»»»

Notes »

Getting Things Done For The Week of: _____

things to do

Habit Tracker

HABIT	S	M	T	W	T	F	S	REWARD

Water
(Check The Circle For 8 Glass Daily)

SUN	MON	TUES	WED	THUR	FRI	SAT
○○○○○	○○○○○	○○○○○	○○○○○	○○○○○	○○○○○	○○○○○
○○○○○	○○○○○	○○○○○	○○○○○	○○○○○	○○○○○	○○○○○

3 Things I am Thankful For »

7 Goals For Next Week »»»»

Notes »

Getting Things Done For The Week of: _____

things to do

Habit Tracker

HABIT	S	M	T	W	T	F	S	REWARD

Water
(Check The Circle For 8 Glass Daily)

SUN	MON	TUES	WED	THUR	FRI	SAT
○○○○	○○○○	○○○○	○○○○	○○○○	○○○○	○○○○
○○○○	○○○○	○○○○	○○○○	○○○○	○○○○	○○○○

girl you got this!

3 Things I am Thankful For »

7 Goals For Next Week »»»»

Notes »

Getting Things Done For The Week of: _____

things to do

Habit Tracker

HABIT	S	M	T	W	T	F	S	REWARD

Water
(Check The Circle For 8 Glass Daily)

SUN	MON	TUES	WED	THUR	FRI	SAT
○○○○	○○○○	○○○○	○○○○	○○○○	○○○○	○○○○
○○○○	○○○○	○○○○	○○○○	○○○○	○○○○	○○○○

girl you got this!

3 Things I am Thankful For »

7 Goals For Next Week »»»»

Notes »

Getting Things Done For The Week of: _____

things to do

Habit Tracker

HABIT	S	M	T	W	T	F	S	REWARD

Water
(Check The Circle For 8 Glass Daily)

SUN	MON	TUES	WED	THUR	FRI	SAT
○○○○	○○○○	○○○○	○○○○	○○○○	○○○○	○○○○
○○○○	○○○○	○○○○	○○○○	○○○○	○○○○	○○○○

girl you got this!

Dreams I made Happen This Month

"

There's a big
difference between
gratitude for your life
and blind acceptance
of whatever comes
your way.
- Rachel Hollis

Note

Who you are is defined by the next decision you make, not the last one.

- Rachel Hollis

Thanks

We Congratulate you for taking that
ultimate decision
And buying this Journal, we hope you'll
achieve
All Your Goals this New Year. Girl, You Got
This!
Take out a little of your Time To Post
A Review For Us on Amazon.

Also we appreciate you for believing in Us
and Buying this Journal. May all Your
Dreams Come through this Year!

Visit: **Cobis Cute Press** on **amazon.com** for more
of this Journal to Help you achieve all your
Dreams For The Year.

Made in the USA
Middletown, DE
04 May 2020

93565837R00066